PUBLISHERS
OF HOPE

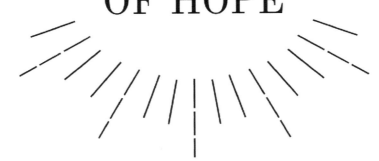

For Some Bunny Special!

Name: _____

Born On: _____

Love: _____

_____

ISBN: 9781735329802 (HC)
ISBN: 9781735329819 (PB)

BUNNY IS BORN

Written By Evan B. Williams
Artwork by Toby Mikle

Once upon a time,

two bunnies
fell in love.

They were happy bunnies, but two bunnies weren't enough.

They prayed and prayed that God might bless their home...

And God answered their prayer, with a baby bunny of their own.

A bunny was born, a true blessing, what joy!

The most precious gift from God, a little bunny boy.

It's a feeling of love, so deep and so wide.

A feeling of love that can't be described.

He's a perfect baby bunny
in his parents' eyes.

He's a small little bunny, so tiny and sweet...

...but soon he'll be running on his feet that he eats.

They'll watch bunny grow
and reach his full potential...

Love, patience, and kindness are essential.

He will change by the minute and before they even know it...

He'll be a big bunny boy,
so they'll cherish
every moment.

The journey won't be easy and challenges will come...

But so will a lifetime of happiness and fun.

So in the face of every challenge...

They will always remember,
how much they've been blessed.

Family Prayer

Thank you for everything you've given us, Lord. Especially the amazing family you've blessed us with.

Please watch over our family, and keep us healthy, happy, and full of love – love for you, and love for each other.

Help us to raise an exceptional person – someone who knows you, and someone who makes the world a better place.

When times are difficult, help us to remember that you won't give us more than we can handle.

Being a parent helps us better understand the relationship we have with you as our Heavenly Father.
Thank you for that perspective.

Please continue to bless and protect this family. Thank you for everything, Lord.

Amen.

For Maverick

CPSIA information can be obtained at www.ICGtesting.com
Printed in the USA
BVIW120223230820
586900BV00013BA/153